SHAME: CONCEPTION

WRITTEN BY LOVERN KINDZIERSKI
INTERIOR AND COVER ART BY JOHN BOLTON
LETTERS AND COVER DESIGN BY TODD KLEIN
EDITOR ALEXANDER FINBOW

RENEGADE
ARTS ENTERTAINMENT

Shame: Conception
Book 1 of the Shame Trilogy
Published by Renegade Arts Canmore Ltd, trading as Renegade Arts Entertainment Ltd
Office of publication: 25 Prospect Heights, Canmore, Alberta, T1W 2S2 Canada
Renegade Arts Entertainment Ltd and its logos are TM and copyright Renegade Arts Canmore Ltd
website: renegadeartsentertainment.com

Renegade Arts Entertainment is
Alexander Finbow Doug Bradley Alan Grant
John Finbow Nick Wilson Jennifer Taylor

ISBN 9781908217011

First Printed 2011
Second Printing 2015

Printed in Canada by Friesens

DEDICATIONS

LOVERN KINDZIERSKI

For Pamela - for her faith in my literary fumbling and the support of her love.

JOHN BOLTON

To Liliana for keeping me on this planet!

INTRODUCTION

I think that this all started with my father. He would carry me, like Tiny Tim, on his shoulders to the drug store to buy his weekly supply of comics. Then we would head back to the apartment above the family store, where he would sit down on the floor with me cradled in his lap. He would hold up the comics for me to watch as he read through them.

Later, when I was old enough to have an allowance, I returned to the drug store to buy comics of my own. Stories about everyone from the Mouse to the Devil. I remember reading through the rack of new comics trying to figure out if I would buy the latest Superboy or Classics Illustrated's Faust. It would always depend on the villains. I guess you could say that I was drawn to the dark side.

So it was no surprise that decades later, as we drove out to our honeymoon hideaway, that the story I chose to entertain my new bride with, was about the nastiest woman that ever lived.

What started out as a way to keep me awake on the highway grew into the story that you have in your hands.

My wife had my pen and notepad on the table with breakfast the next morning, and I didn't get to play until I had written out this first part of Shame's story and had some notes of the story to follow.

I hope that you will enjoy it as much as Pamela did.

Lovern Kindzierski May 9th 2011

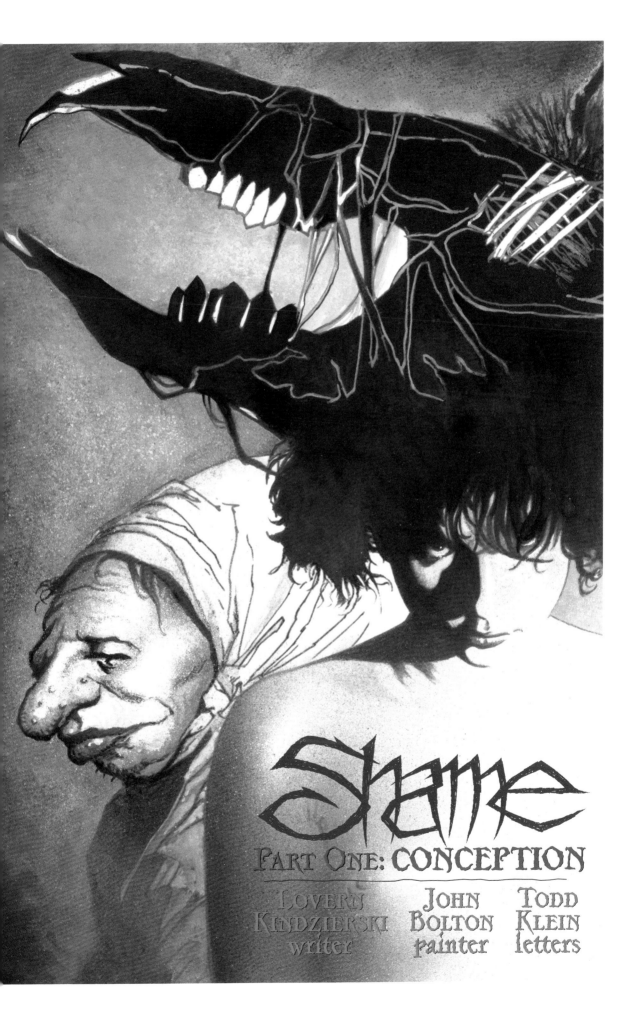

Shame

PART ONE: CONCEPTION

LOVERN
KINDZIERSKI
writer

JOHN
BOLTON
painter

TODD
KLEIN
letters

Yet each evening she had to bid them goodbye.

MOTHER VIRTUE! WAIT FOR ME!

I PICKED YOU A SPECIAL FLOWER!

TO THANK YOU FOR MAKING MY EARS BETTER!

LOVE YOU.

I LOVE YOU TOO, HOLLY.

BYE!

BYE!

BYE BYE, CHILDREN.

miss you...

Mother Virtue dwelt apart from all the bustle of the village with its little families. The garden provided her with comfort and the herbs and plants necessary to her magicks.

The quiet and solitude rejuvenated the old woman and soothed her soul...for the most part...

NOW, WHAT TREASURES DO I HAVE TO ADD TO MY TROVE?

OH! LITTLE HOLLY'S FLOWER.

SUCH A LOVELY CHILD.

I'VE CARED FOR SO MANY CHILDREN, BUT NEVER ONE OF MY OWN. NEVER MET THE RIGHT MAN AND NOW THAT TIME HAS PASSED. OH, BUT IF I HAD ONE WISH IT WOULD SURELY BE FOR A CHILD.

MY *DAUGHTER!* NOT ONE THAT I SHARE.

SURELY I DESERVE THAT MUCH.

AH, ME! WISHING AND DAYDREAMING WON'T GET SUPPER ON THE FIRE.

Sadly, as often is the case, Mother Virtue's selfish wish echoed like a dinner bell in the Heart of Darkness...

...where, waiting for such an opportunity, lay a dark, dark evil.

Several weeks crept by and Mother Virtue began to notice subtle changes in her body. Possibilities long ago laid to rest.

She threw the bones of a snow-white crow and read the fate they spelled out.

Then up from the flames rose Slur! The Shadow of Ignorance!

OH YES, DEAR MOTHER VIRTUE! A *BLACK SEED* GROWS IN YOUR BARREN WOMB. PLANTED BY YOUR WISH AND QUICKENED BY MY MAGICK, FOR *GOD* WOULD NEVER HEAR SUCH SELFISH WORDS!

FORGET ALL THOUGHT OF SWEEPING THIS OFF THE HEARTH WITH YOUR WHITE MEDDLING. THE CHILD'S SOUL IS *FIXED* AND THERE IS NAUGHT YOU CAN DO ABOUT IT. SHE EVEN KNOWS HER NAME. IT IS *SHAME!*

The richness of the flora grew with the swelling of her womb.

This in turn drew all the dryads and nymphs from the surrounding forest. The song of Mother Virtue's white magic coaxed them out of hiding.

And once they revealed themselves, Mother Virtue's spell bound them to her humble cottage and its environs.

This link in the spell being completed, the cottage itself grew and became a living home in which Mother Virtue's child would grow safely.

She called the living thing it had become: *Cradle*.

Months passed away.

Then, with a small cry, **Shame** was born into the world.

As Mother Virtue's body had prepared itself for the birth of her child, so had the bodies of some of the dryads who now dwelt with her.

Cradle's spell bound all within this magickal garden to the purpose of raising and sustaining Shame. The nymphs and dryads would be her nurses and her caretakers.

Cradle would also be Shame's prison. She might dwell in our world, but she would not be a part of it, and Slur's dominion over the Earth would be curtailed. Mother Virtue could not chance that she herself might be the weak link. She must abandon her child. And as Mother Virtue left, the forest grew up behind her, forming a barrier that none could pass.

Six years have passed and Shame is a little girl now. Her nurse maids have become playmates.

Play, as it sometimes does, leads to small cruelties.

Cruelty--being the element of Shame's conception--

--unveils the power that lies within her.

The game ends with a lesson learned by all. A lesson that Shame is unlikely to forget.

Especially when Shame can *exploit* the lesson herself.

In no time at all Shame finds that she can shape her little world to the dictates of her will.

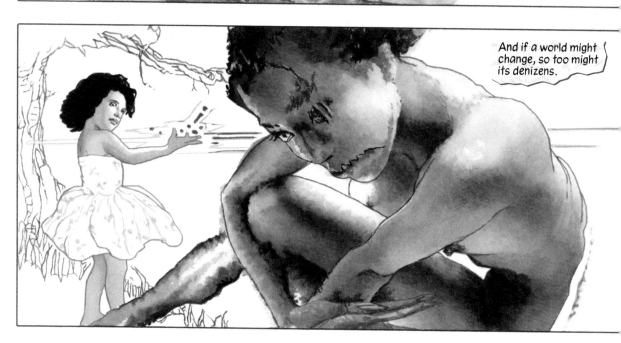

And if a world might change, so too might its denizens.

Outside of Cradle the world moves along in its way. The impassable forest is now mostly ignored by Man. Unfortunately, children do not always follow the advice of their elders.

The games they play can often lead them astray.

Then, some of the more daring children can take the games farther yet.

LOOK-- INSIDE THE FOREST!

This often leads them to discover just why a forbidden place does not make a playground.

OUR SHADOWS LOOK SO DIFFERENT.

BUT LOOK AT THE TREES!

MISTRESS! YOU MUST BE CAREFUL!

NO NO NO NO...

YOU MUST NOT--

I MUST AND I SHALL!

The fog is lifted. Shame's mind begins to clear. Now her warders and guards will begin to fear.

Shame knows her home is a tether which now she cannot conquer.

Cold fires in her heart do smoulder for Shadows with news of her father.

The Shadows make many more visits and warp the fabric of Virtue's spell by teaching Shame more and more of her Father's ways.

With your power you fold water into a ball.

Then push it up so tall.

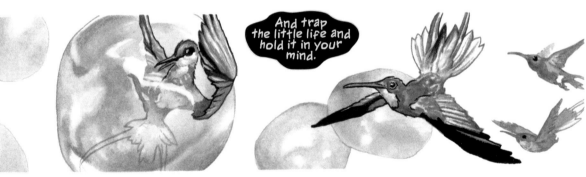

And trap the little life and hold it in your mind.

As the bird's life flees it is trapped in the ball, and now the globe can be so much more.

It can be a third eye to see what your others cannot. And all you need is a thought.

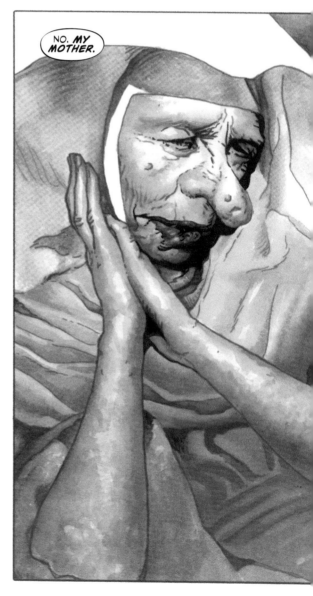

The time it was indeed. Shame's darkness within Cradle had grown so that now Slur could breach the spell that protected his daughter from him.

And so that very night...

SHAME

DAUGHTER

All within Shame's prison realm respond to her touch.

OWW!

IDIOT!

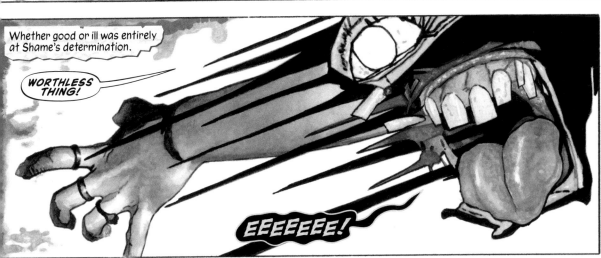

Whether good or ill was entirely at Shame's determination.

WORTHLESS THING!

EEEEEEE!

And Shame had little regard for anything she could replace.

LACKEY! A REPLACEMENT DRESSER. NOW!

Yes, mistress!

Off to a place not so far from Shame's prison. To a dwelling place of men.

Then--clothed in woman's flesh...

...the demon went about its carnal craft.

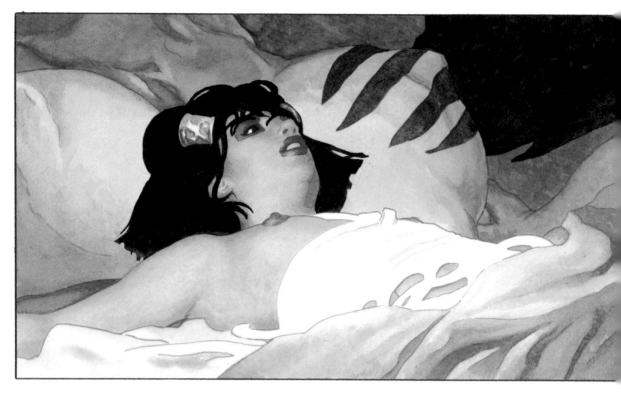

Nine long months have passed.

Cradle and its grounds reek with the smell of oils torn from the living plants and creatures of the darkling glade.

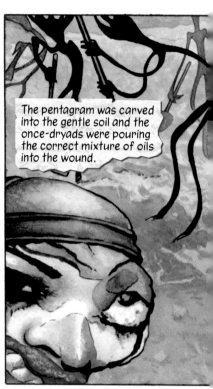

The pentagram was carved into the gentle soil and the once-dryads were pouring the correct mixture of oils into the wound.

CAREFUL WITH THAT MIXTURE OR YOU'LL BE IN THE *PRESS* FOR THE NEXT BATCH!

And so proceeded the plans for the night of revenge!

A few nights later the moment had arrived.

O ETERNUS QUOD OMNIPOTENS ISOGOG!

EGO QUESO THEE UT PATEFACIO IANUA INTER REGNUM.

The terrified servants quickly hustled Shame into the birthing room.

Unlike her own peaceful birth Shame's contractions were laden with the pain of her misdeeds.

AAAARRR BARGAIN! REMEMBER THE BARGAIN!

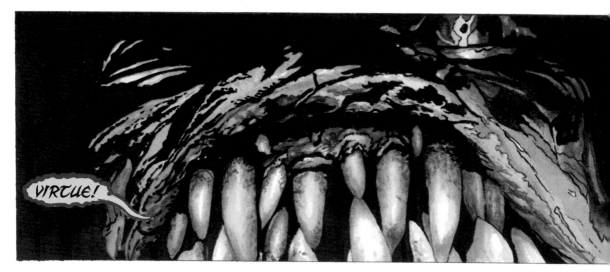

Lovern Kindzierski

Lovern is a successful writer, colorist and illustrator based in Winnipeg, Canada.

His colors have appeared in many comic books and magazines including; *The X-men*, *Star Trek*, *Dr. Who*, *The New Yorker, Wired,* and *Sesame Street*.

He has been nominated as best colorist for the Eisner Awards, Harvey Awards, and Schuster Awards. Lovern has won The Wizard Fan best colorist award (twice), as well as the Comic Buyers' Guide Best Colorist Fan Award. The co-founder of Digital Chameleon in 1991, his computer colouring pioneered digital comics colouring.

For Renegade, Lovern is colorist on the eagerly anticipated *The Loxley's and the War of 1812* comic book, the multi-lingual *Arctic Comics*, William Simpson's Vampire comic book series *VMT*, and Alexander Finbow's *24 Days In Rio*.

As a writer, he has worked on titles including *Spiderman, Wolverine*, and *The Victorian*. His writing on *Tarzan* garnered him a Harvey Award Best Writer nomination.

As well as writing the *Shame* trilogy for Renegade, Lovern is currently writing a new supernatural comic book series entitled *Necromantic*, with Rafael Kayanan on art duties.

John Bolton

Based in London, England, and described by director Robert Rodriguez as a "God" for his art in Peter Straub's *The Green Woman*, John was seven when he first encountered a paint brush. It was love at first sight, offering him an output to visualize and create what he saw in his mind and put it to paper. Thus began a life-long ambition of creativity, with influences acquired from a wide variety of sources, but all connected by one underlying theme, the interesting and bizarre.

Bolton's innovative approach to sequential art has seen him rise to the very top of the current crop of artists working in comics. He digs deep into his imagination to come up with something never seen before. His painting displays a thorough understanding of each medium and subject he chooses to tackle.

His inspiration comes not from outside influences, but from the story he is illustrating, the style stems from the content and emotion of a particular story.

John has collaborated with a host of prestigious writers including Chris Claremont, Mike Carey, Neil Gaiman, Clive Barker and Mark Verheiden. As well as filmmakers Sam Raimi, Jonathan Glazer, and Robert Zemeckis.

Shame: Conception marks John's first work for Renegade, but with painting well underway for book 2 of the trilogy, the foundations have been laid for a long and successful relationship.

RENEGADE
ARTS ENTERTAINMENT

Shame

PURSUIT

2 of 3

COMING
2012

LOVERN KINDZIERSKI JOHN BOLTON TODD KLEIN

MORE TITLES FROM RENEGADE ARTS ENTERTAINMENT

Shades of Grey
24 Hours in London
One-shot Comic
Writer: Alexander Finbow
Art: William Simpson

Out Now

Shades of Grey
24 Days in Rio
One-shot Comic
Writer: Alexander Finbow
Art: William Simpson

*Release Date:
October 2011*

V.M.T
6 Issue Series
Creator: William Simpson

*Release Date:
October 2011*

Turning Tiger Collected Edition
2 Issue Series
Writer: Richmond Clements
Art: Alex Moore

Release Date: August 2011

Monsterology 101
Ongoing Comic Series
Writer: Gordon Rennie
Art: P.J. Holden

*Release Date:
October 2011*

Doug Bradley's Spinechillers
Classic Horror Audiobooks
Volumes 1-13
Writers: Various

Out Now

**Channel Evil
Collected Edition**
4 Issue Series
Writer: Alan Grant
Art: Shane Oakley

Release Date: 2012

The Loxley's & The War of 1812
140 page Comic Book
Writer: Alan Grant
Art: Claude St. Aubin

Release Date: December 2011

Blood Light
180 page Comic Book
Writer: Alexander Finbow
Art: Al Davison

Release Date: 2012

Granny's Attic
A Tale of Curious Critters
Illustrated children's book
Writer: Liz Dodsworth
Illustrator: Liz Dodsworth

Out Now

Arctic Comics
Anthology Comic Book
Creators: Various

Release Date: 2012